Ten Thousand Days
of Summer

Ten Thousand Days of Summer

~•~

*The Story of the Boy
who would be Buddha*

WRITTEN BY
Andrea Willson

ILLUSTRATED BY
Andy Weber

wellseeing
books

First published in 2009 by
Wellseeing Books
1 Barn Garth
Haverthwaite
Cumbria
LA12 8AE

in association with
Long House Publishing Services

Front cover illustration by Andy Weber
Designed and set by Long House Publishing Services
Printed in Great Britain by CPI Antony Rowe Chippenham and Eastbourne

ISBN 978-0-9556437-1-2

Contents

Acknowledgements

I would like to thank the following people who have supported me at one time or another on the journey of this book:

Lama Zopa Rinpoche, Ven. Roger Kunsang, Ven. Robina Courtin, Natalee Staviss, Nick Ribush, Wisdom Publications, Shambhala Publications, Cody Sanders, Joey Weber, Liza Weber, Chris Stark, Liz Drew, Ian Davidson, Beverley McArthur, Caroline Winsor, Katie Tiley and especially to my partner Andy Weber who provided the wonderful artwork and who never let me give up.

This book would still be sitting unpublished on a shelf if it had not been for the kind generosity of these sponsors and benefactors:

Babs and Ken Oxley
Marjory Miller
Yeshe Buddhist Centre
Hugh Clift

Many thanks to Glenn Mullin for his gracious introduction.

Foreword

In India at the time of the Buddha, spiritual and religious teachings were considered so sacred that they were not written down. When the Buddha started teaching, this custom still existed and so when he taught, every word had to be remembered. Numbers are a good way to know if you have remembered everything you should. The Buddha gave 84,000 teachings throughout his life, and being a good teacher, he used numbers to identify them: The Three Jewels, The Four Noble Truths, The Eightfold Path – so if you found yourself remembering only three Noble Truths you were one missing. What he said must have been amazing because all his teachings *were* remembered and eventually written down.

But his life itself, not his teachings, is the door through which we can find the boy and the man who became Buddha and begin to understand what kind of a person he was, grasp the essence of his life and perhaps understand our own a little better. It speaks of the possibilities and potential of us all and poses deep, important questions about life and it's meaning; and it is as timeless and relevant to people now as it was 2,500 years ago when Prince

Siddhartha was born. Simply as a story, it is wonderful: a quest with a hero, a journey and a seemingly impossible treasure. Also, it means you won't have to read 84,000 texts to find out a little about Buddhism!

I wrote this when I was pregnant with my first child who is now twenty-two so it has taken me about 8,000 days to put this into your hands and has been a mini quest of my own. The script rested, like an out-of-work actor, in the wings of my life until the time was finally right to publish it. Stories about religious people are difficult to get right. There are the facts and evidence of their life but these are woven together with stories and myths and often include miracles. Some say the miracles are exaggerations by people who want their heroes to appear superhuman. Some say there is no exaggeration because very special spiritual people really do perform miracles.

My retelling has its share of magic and the miraculous, and it is an accurate historical account. I have then dressed it with an imagining of what might have been thought, felt and spoken to give it warmth and life. It focuses on the time when the Buddha was just a boy and young man, shakes the dust off his bones and adds flesh and blood, thoughts and feelings to a waxwork legend. It charts 10,000 "perfect" days before he finally started to remove the dust from his eyes and see things more clearly. Fortunately for me, his life was so comfortable that it took him longer than the average child to want to leave home, so my story is long enough to be a book. Not wishing to push the numbers thing, one hundred and ten pages to be precise.

The Buddha and all Buddhist teachers since him say that

you should test any idea and theory as thoroughly as if you were testing gold and accept only that which seems right to you. So make up your own mind about what you believe in. Perhaps all that matters is that you believe in yourself. The Buddha did.

Andrea Willson
Haverthwaite
February 2009

"In the language of Angels,
Of serpents, of fairies,
In the speech of the demons,
The talk of the humans,
In them all I have taught
The Dharma's* deep teachings,
And in any tongue
That a being may grasp them."

Shakyamuni Buddha*

* See glossary on page 115

Introduction
Glenn H. Mullin

The life of the Buddha, his Great Enlightenment, and his work in establishing a living legacy for training and elevating the mind, has been an inspiration to hundreds of millions of people in Asia for more than 2,500 years now. It has been told and retold, generation after generation, with an inexhaustible enthusiasm. The tradition began with the great Indian masters, and then was continued in the many countries where the enlightenment legacy took deep root: Sri Lanka, Thailand, Tibet, Mongolia, China, Japan, Korea and more.

In her wonderful little book *Ten Thousand Days of Summer: The Story of the Boy who would be Buddha*, Andrea Willson has brought the tale into the modern, international arena, retelling it with the magic and wonder that has captivated audiences over the centuries. It is a great read, a profound wave of joyful literary indulgence, and a magnificent contribution to the growing corpus of literature on the Buddha, his life, and his vision of human perfection. Andrea is indeed a talented storyteller.

The illustrations by the master artist Andy Weber, with whom I have personally had the opportunity to work on a number of writing projects, add to the flavour of the narrative. The blending of words and images draw the reader into an intimacy of experience equal to the impact of the illuminated texts that were so popular in bygone eras, when people took time to create books that were not only literarily uplifting, but were also a feast for the aesthetic eye.

Glenn H Mullin
Winter Solstice
Mongolia, 2008

To Joey and Liza

CHAPTER ONE

Queen Maya's Dream

Crystal star
dazzling in
the dark sky.
Sharp blade-bright
Icicle fronds
cutting the
night's black.

Heavenly sounds
like bees' hums,
distant drums,
angelic yearning

and I'm turning
and swirling
in wild white
searing flight,
Dissolved in,
absorbed in
liquid
light.

Now he's clear.
Purple eyes
probing mine.
Six white tusks
pierce my skin,
then enter in.

I'm drowned
in light and
the white night.

Majestic
creature
come from the
sky like a
god sent gift
to become
simply a
part of
me.

Then light fades
leaving just
the night
quite quiet,
washing me
dreamlessly
to sleep.

All but a
flame inside,
a small glow
glimmering,
and deeper,
deeper, deep.
From deeper
than where the
dragons sleep,
young blood
beats.

CHAPTER TWO
Wise Words and a Birth

Queen Maya sat up. She'd just had the strangest dream and she needed to tell someone. But the dream feeling wasn't fading so perhaps she wasn't awake? She noticed that everything around her seemed intense and vivid; even her own body felt different. Was she floating above the bed? Her long lustrous hair, curled by sleep, coiled round her arms like amiable, sleeping snakes and the air kissed her lips good morning. The blue sky beyond the balcony spilled into her room and spread itself upon her sheets and the smells of the summer flowers intoxicated her.

The Queen always enjoyed the early morning. In the first hours after dawn, the world seemed fresh and perfect. But today, if she was really awake, then she'd died and gone to heaven. She stretched like a warm, well-fed cat, and shook herself loose from her sleepiness. Padma, her grumpy parrot, was perched at the end of her bed, just like every other morning, making a show of sharpening his beak

on something he had stolen from the Queen's dressing table. Usually, the Queen would pretend to be cross, and Padma would get some attention, but this morning she just whooshed back the sheets and laughed at him.

Squawking with shock, Padma dropped the trinket and flew frenziedly around the room. The Queen was immediately concerned and urged him to come to her.

"I'm sorry, Padma," she cooed soothingly, settling him on to her shoulder. "I didn't mean to upset you."

She felt the bird's blind fear as she stroked away his shivers, and a tear fell from her eye. "Om Namo Shiva-ji,"* she sighed. "How can I be happy when you are not?"

Then, recalling the cause of her happiness, she called for her attendants. One to help her dress. One to take a message to the King. And one to fetch the Royal Sages.*

5

The Royal Sages were just finishing their meditation, peacefully watching the palace come to life from the veranda in front of their rooms. Each morning, before they did anything other than yawn, they sat silent and still, contemplating the Great Meaning of Life. Their job as advisers to the King and Queen, was to become as wise as possible and to give wise advice – otherwise their advice would be useless. So, sitting in deep thought and meditation became the major part of their work. In fact, they were so skilled, that just as a carpenter can make a chair from a log, and a farmer can reap a harvest of corn from a handful of seeds, so they could turn their thoughts into Wisdom.

Their old knees cracked as they unwound their legs and got up. When the Queen's messenger arrived, they were scooping the black seeds out of sun-warmed, rosy papayas, and preparing to eat their breakfast.

"I'm sssorry to disturb yyyyou" stammered the young boy, horribly nervous in their presence, "but the Queen wishes to see you ... At once!"

Within minutes, the wise and awesome men stood before the King and Queen. When Queen Maya had finished telling them her dream, they pulled thoughtfully on their long, white beards and put their heads together......

King Shuddodhana tried to remain calm. He could feel his wife's slight body shudder in his arms and pulled her closer. The importance of the dream was beginning to make itself felt.

"There's no doubt about it!" exclaimed the first royal adviser.

"A most wonderful blessing!" proclaimed the second. "You are very fortunate indeed!" smiled the third. The King was losing his patience. "Well?!" he spluttered. "What does it all mean?"

"O King, the queen's dream holds meaning and foretells of a great event", said the first Sage. " The white elephant symbolises a gift of spiritual power and purity; his six tusks represent the six great states of mind: giving, goodness, patience, effort, meditation and wisdom; the purple eyes are the sign of royalty amongst royalty." "Make sense," snapped the King, confused by their signs and omens. The second sage quickly got to the point, "You are soon to become a mother, dearest queen and your child will be a son, blessed with the most unusual talents. These talents will make him a great man. Our small kingdom will shine with the light of his wisdom, and all the kingdoms to the north, south, west and east of our land, and all the countries in the world will benefit from his birth."

There was a long, deep silence as the five people reflected on the dream and its meaning. Somewhere in the corner, a lizard coughed; outside, the birds gossiped. The royal advisers meaningfully stroked their beards, then silently bowed their way out.

The King and Queen needed time to reflect on their news and walked through the palace gardens alone together. Amongst the fountains and flowers, they shared their thoughts. They talked of the dream, its significance and the reality of having a child and gradually their excitement became real. They planned and then they wondered and they planned and then they worried about this special boy who would one day be King. And when they looked into the fountain's reflections they saw themselves and in the space beside them was a dark haired boy with eyes as deep as the ocean.

The months passed, and if the image in her mirror had not told otherwise, the Queen might have questioned if she were indeed pregnant. She did not feel sick, tired, or swollen. Her step was as quick, her days as long as ever before. Sometimes she did have the urge to hold onto a chair or table, but not for support. She feared she was so light that she might float away! But with her secret knowledge and her unshakeable serenity, the Queen carried her baby like oil in a bowl, and regarded him like treasure locked in a vault.

Since it was customary in India in those days for women to return to the home of their parents to give birth, the King made arrangements for the Queen's journey to her

old childhood home. Nothing was to be spared for her comfort and safety. The day of the journey arrived. Begging her to take care, the anxious King fondly kissed his wife and waved farewell. Queen Maya settled amongst the cushions, gazed from her carriage as it carried her away from the palace, and enjoyed the colourful sights along the way. People were busy living their lives. Men squatted at the teashops, drinking, chatting and exchanging gossip. Women walked with heavy baskets balanced high upon their heads, and talked in doorways, their bright saris splashing the dusty streets like paint. As the royal procession passed, the streets filled with excitement. The Queen sighed, content that everything was as it should be. For everyone a place, she thought, and a place for everyone.

Then she wondered, as she wondered so much these days, about her baby boy. Would he look like her handsome husband? Would he share her love of poetry and music? Would he take after her family or the King's?

Her mind flashed back to the day she had first heard the prediction and the words of the Sages she now knew by heart. She was so proud to think that she would mother a man whose power would influence the world. But she knew that power meant war and wondered how many would have to be fought for him to have such an enormous influence on the world, and her forehead wrinkled, disturbed by the thought of violence and fighting.

Then, quite suddenly, but quite calmly, Queen Maya knew that she must stop the royal procession. She looked from her carriage and saw the beautiful gardens of Lumbini and wanted to be out there. She wanted to wash in the clear waters of the cool glades. She wanted to have her baby here.

Waving to her dismayed courtiers to stay where they were, she walked slowly through the trees and flowers. The trees appeared to her to bow as she passed and she felt safe beside their strength. She stopped, and raising her left arm, felt a firm branch rest into her hand. With the tree supporting her, she gave birth.

The woman and child lay together beneath the tree. Here in the garden, and now at this time, there was no palace, no inheritance, no future. For a brief, cherished moment, there was nothing for the Queen but the joy of her love.

Slowly, her curious companions tiptoed round. The Queen raised her head and the baby opened his eyes. He blinked, and then they were sure that he smiled. Here he was, in the world.

~•~

While this was taking place at Lumbini, life was going on as usual elsewhere. At the same time as the Queen walked through the gardens, yet another argument had started at Shivanath's Tea Shop. Mr Shivanath and his three sons were the proud proprietors of the village's only teashop. The youngest boy was just bringing some tea to a customer when he tripped, and cup and contents landed in the unfortunate customer's lap.

13

14

"Mani, you clumsy boy! Can't you watch what you are doing? Pouring the profit away like that!" Shivanath yelled at him.

"Father, please don't shout. Everyone can hear you. Why must you always embarrass me in this way?" hissed the boy.

"What have I done to deserve such sons?" Shivanath asked no one in particular. "Well, don't just stand there! Get a cloth! Do something!" he cried.

"How can I do anything when you're shouting at me? Why don't you ask my lazy brother to do something for a change?" He challenged his father.

"Oh, go soak you head. You're always whining!" This was Kabir, the eldest of the three. He was standing beside the sweet cabinet, cleaning his nails with a knife and watching the girls go by. Kumar, the middle son, was washing glasses. He was a hard worker and ambitious. He had plans to extend the old teashop and attract travellers passing through.

"Why don't you all shut up! How can we maintain our good name with all this bickering going on in public? You'll frighten off all the customers." He snapped.

"Pardon me, but what about my tea? And look at what you've done to my best clothes." Interrupted the old man, who was the only customer.

"Oh keep out of this! It was all your fault anyway, coming here and causing trouble between a father and his sons. Have you no shame?" accused Shivanath.

"How dare you speak to me like that! I WILL NOT be spoken to like that! I WILL NOT! I WILL NOT, DO YOU HEAR?!" The man with the damp lap was by now hysterical.

"Oh shut up, you silly old goat!" The three sons spoke all at once.

The old man's mouth fell open in astonishment. All at once, time and emotions seemed suspended.

For a moment, everyone stood transfixed. The village suddenly became like a stage set, the people players in a silent tableau. Suspended in laughter or tears, dark with hate, drawn with pain, or lit with feverish hope, every man, woman and child's face told it's own story.

Shivanath was looking up from the spot where he crouched next to the fire brewing endless pots of tea and tossing chapattis.* His eyes rested on the lonely and tormented eyes of the old man. He looked surprised to see such sorrow. The three bothers stood isolated by their anger. Mani bitterly squeezed out a wet cloth. Kabir aggressively pierced the air with his knife as if it were a sword. Kumar's hands hovered possessively over the box where they kept the takings. Realising they had spoken the very same words to the old man at the very same instant, they had turned their faces toward each other and now shared the same expression of astonishment. Then, as if a magic wand had been waved about, the village returned to life. Everyone felt the peculiarity of the moment, and experienced tingling which started somewhere in their toes and ended up somewhere in their heads. Frustrations and fears melted away; conflicts and attachments were forgotten. The people sensed that something strange and inexplicable had happened, but could not pin down the magic. All they knew was that somehow they had been transformed. Suddenly, for an intense brief moment in

time, they all felt happy.

In the teashop, Shivanath spoke first. "Well, let's all stop this silly nonsense. After all, accidents can happen!" He laughed.

"Yes, let's be friends," Mani said as he good naturedly hugged Kabir. Kumar put his arm around the old man's shoulders.

"Come on, let's have tea together," he said. "It's on the house!"

"What a jolly good idea," smiled the old man, who had only gone to the teashop for the company anyway.

So, they patted each other on the back and assured each other they were all remarkable fellows. As they hugged, each slowly began to realise how much he liked the others. After years of bickering across tabletops and dirty cups, at last they felt in harmony. And how good it was! How warm the shoulder beneath the hand, how kind the smiling eyes. Laughter welled up from deep inside them, bubbled for a moment upon their disconcerted lips, and then, like dams bursting, floodgates opening, volcanoes erupting ... hot springs springing ... they cried! Suddenly, an explosion of pent-up emotion rocked the whole village and soon everyone was crying and laughing, laughing and crying at the same time.

Everyone was doing the sort of thing you do when a war is ended or a fortune is won. A man danced gleefully round the tired, old horse he had just been cursing, a sick woman got out of bed and threw open the shutters. A boy returned the pomegranate he had just stolen. The dogs stopped fighting. A hungry cat dropped the mouse she had just caught and licked it better. The mouse sat peacefully without fear. Even the flies stopped bothering the cows. Everyone and everything was happy! And soon Mr. Shivanath was making large kettles of milky tea and his sons were filling the cups, not half-full but right to the brim, and giving them away with ginger cakes – free!! Surely, something wonderful had happened.

Even the sort of people who go around kicking innocent dogs could be seen bending down and patting bony backs that day. And as brilliant rainbows appeared in the sky, though there had been no rain for weeks, and spectacular

lights burst out in the heavens like god-flung fireworks, everyone agreed that the sky was indeed bluer, the tea creamier, the fruit juicier, their friends funnier, the sun sunnier and life just BETTER than ever before.

No one knew why the world was suddenly a better place to live in. No one knew what had happened to change it, but everyone in the entire kingdom experienced the same strange joy that day. The day Prince Siddhartha was born.

CHAPTER THREE
Childhood and Lessons

It doesn't matter how rich you are. It doesn't matter if you live in a palace or a pot-hole. You can still lose someone you love. Soon after Siddhartha was born, his mother, the Queen everyone loved, died. King Shuddhodana cried for three weeks. One was for his wife – "She was too young to die!" One was for himself – "How can I live without her!" And one week was for his son – "Who will take care of the boy and love him like a mother?" Then, he stopped crying. He had no tears left.

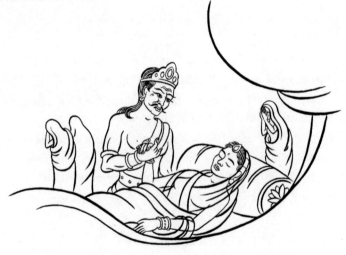

Soon after this, Prajapati, the Queen's sister, came to see the King. She had dearly loved her sister and was the only person the Queen had trusted as much as her husband.

"I will take care of Siddhartha," she said. "The boy will not have to suffer without a mother. I will take her place." So, Prajapati became Siddhartha's second mother. Siddhartha never knew his real mother, so he could not miss her. But the King did. Sometimes, Siddhartha would look up to see his father staring away into the distance, as if his mind were somewhere far away. Solemnly, Siddhartha would approach the King and gently tug on the sleeve of his cloak until he attracted his father's attention. Seeing his son gazing up at him so seriously, the King would smile in wonder. Siddhartha was still a child, but already he knew the King better than his oldest friends did.

The little Prince endeared himself to all in the palace. He knew all the birds and animals in the gardens and he knew all the flowers. He knew the girls who worked in the laundry and he knew the boy who swept the leaves in the courtyard. He knew the old blind man who lived in the stables and fed the horses. No one escaped the attention of his knowing, old eyes and he loved them all as they loved him. He didn't chase or scare the birds or tease the cats, and if he was asked to do a favour, he didn't get cheeky and run away. He was kind to everyone and everything, as if he knew what it was

21

like to BE them. He loved flowers, but he didn't pick them. He loved animals but didn't cage them. He loved people, but he had no favourites. He enjoyed life for what it was, not for what it could give to him. Others' happiness made him happy. Everyone in the kingdom took an interest in this remarkable child and many would shake their heads in wonder when they heard the many tales of his wisdom and kindness.

~•~

It was ploughing time, the time of year when the earth is turned and the people pray for a good harvest. The King himself drove the first pair of bullocks through the fields, and the noble lords and farmers followed. The people stood watching and threw rice into the air for good luck.

Siddhartha sat beneath an apple tree and watched the ceremony. His father, he thought, looked very grand. He wore gold ornaments in his ears and a huge golden crown on his head. His clothes made him look larger than he really was, and the golden brocade of his robes glinted in the sun. Even the bullocks were decorated today, their horns wound in gold thread, with gold painted harnesses and a golden plough to pull. The noblemen were dressed in silver, but though there were many of them, they didn't look quite so grand or sparkle quite so much as the King. Siddhartha smiled because his father looked so proud and happy.

The Royal Sages said special prayers and made offerings to the gods to ensure a plentiful harvest. Then the King roared like a lion and strode off down the field, keeping a plough in a very straight line. Next came the lords and farmers, followed by the people. Siddhartha noticed that some of the villagers kept close to the ploughs, their eyes sifting the churned up earth. What could they be looking for? One man stooped to pick something up, then triumphantly waved a frog by one leg before stuffing it into his pocket. "What is that man going to do with the frog?" Siddhartha asked Prajapati.

"I expect he'll eat it for supper," replied Prajapati. Something landed with a loud thud close by. Siddhartha turned to see a limp snake, smeared with red, that had been thrown away by someone in the crowd.

"What is wrong with that snake? Is it sick?" he asked. "No, it's dead." Answered Prajapati.

Siddhartha stared about him as if dazed with pain. Then, he silently closed his eyes.

Prajapati thought her nephew was resting, so when everyone moved onto another field, she left him in peace, and took a walk through the trees. But Siddhartha was not resting. He was deep in thought. So deeply was he thinking that if someone had rung a bell right next to his ear, he would not have heard it. He had entered a different world where time stood still. At that time in India, there were many wise men, known as Rishis, who had learned to do things that we have been told only witches and wizards and magicians can do. They learned how to hover above the ground. They learned to make objects move without ever touching them. They even learned how to fly. As Siddhartha sat beneath the apple tree, five such men with supernatural powers came flying through the air.

The Rishis had just returned from the great Himalayan mountains and were on their way home. These Rishis would not dream of wasting time on such pointless exercises as washing and good manners. Left alone together in the mountains so high, with the sun and moon so close, they had looked beyond what is considered normal, nice behaviour and their aim was not to impress others as a politician might, but to attain great wisdom and enjoy the freedom that gave them. And sometimes, they seemed to delight in gently mocking the pursuits of ordinary people.

Now, seeing a mere child in deep meditation, they became curious and circled over his head three times before landing a short distance away so they could study this curious sight. They watched him closely, as naturalists might observe an insect, but Siddhartha did not move. However, after a while, the Prince sensed that he was not alone, and he opened his eyes and grinned at the five men. He was not at all put out to see such wild looking creatures, whose hair stood on end from so much flying about and whose eyes glared at him with such intensity.

"May we ask what you are contemplating, young sir?" asked the first Rishi, scratching his armpit with long, dirty nails.

"Yes, we are most interested to hear about what absorbs such a young mind," pursued the second.

"Perhaps you are wondering what you will be when you grow up?" suggested the third, clearing his throat and shooting a goblet of phlegm expertly into the air.

"Or if you will be as handsome as you are now," laughed the fourth Rishi, displaying a mouthful of black stubs.

"Maybe you are trying to think of a way to become the richest man in the world," teased the fifth, and with a huge leap into the air, he lifted the jewelled turban from Siddhartha's head and rakishly propped it on his own. They laughed at his antic so much that Siddhartha thought they would burst, and he started to laugh too, but then he stopped. When his smile turned to sadness, they too stopped laughing. "I will tell you why I am thinking so hard," he said. "Perhaps you can help me understand." And he told them about the grand ceremony, and the Sages' prayers for a good harvest, about his father's fancy dress, and the frog and the snake, and how everyone had enjoyed themselves.

The Rishis smiled mischievously at one another. "Well, it sounds like we missed a good party, boys," sighed one, shaking his head and rolling his eyes melodramatically.

"Yes, it's too bad we came too late," the second agreed slowly, contorting his face into a grimace of regret.

"But we still don't know what you were thinking about," added another. "Were you sad because you're too young to join in the fun?" he pouted, displaying a baby face to delight his friends, but Siddhartha knew they were just testing him and he was not interested in playing their game.

He was upset and a tear appeared in the corner of his eye. "No," he answered, unmoved by their frivolity, "but perhaps it is because I am too young to understand the pleasures of this world." He paused, and the Rishis stopped clowning, silenced by the words that seemed so strange from a child. Siddhartha continued, "While others saw beauty, I saw ugliness. I did not see the pretty bluebird feeding her hungry babies – I saw a dragonfly crushed under her sharp beak, and ripped apart by three small monsters. I did not see the soft-eyed rab-

bits running across the field in freedom; I saw helpless creatures suffering great fear for their homes and families. I did not see a lucky man's supper turned up by the plough, or a useless pest destroyed. I saw a painful death and a life just tossed aside like rubbish. I did not see a joyful festival. I saw only selfishness and ignorance."

Siddhartha stopped and slowly lowered his small, dark head. The Rishis had to lean forward to hear him speak again. "So you see, my friends, that is why I closed my eyes."

The mouths of the Rishis dropped open and their eyes bulged. They could not believe their ears. Was it possible for a child to have such wisdom? They, the clever Rishis, had just learned a great lesson from a child! It had taken them many, many years of contemplation and meditation to reach such a profound level of understanding. And they still had not felt such great compassion. All five of them felt very humble before this young boy. For a long time, they sat quite still, too deeply moved to say or do anything.

Suddenly, five apples dropped from the tree into five laps. Siddhartha had to laugh at the look on their faces. The Rishis laughed too. Soon, they were introducing themselves, eating their applies and vowing undying friendship.

Eventually, they had to leave, for it was getting late. Remembering the turban, the fifth Rishi felt ashamed. Wiping his hands on his filthy rags, he replaced the turban on Siddhartha's head. "You are indeed fit to wear a crown.

Although small you are great. Although young you are old." And with these words, knowing the gods had led them to someone very special, the five Rishis gave prayers of thanks and bowed many times to the young Prince before they flew off towards home.

When the King returned from the celebration, he found his son exactly where he had left him, sitting in the shade of the tree, happily eating apples. But the King had been gone for over two hours and the shadow cast by the tree had not moved! He looked at his son in amazement and dropped to his knees before him. Who was this child for whom even time stood still? This experience at the harvest festival would remain locked inside Siddhartha's mind for many years. Only much, much later would he recall his meditation under the apple tree, and recognise its' value.

~•~

On his first day at school, Siddhartha waited nervously in the classroom with the other children. Mr Mohan, who ran the palace school, was a quiet, stern man with a habit of rubbing his nose when he got cross. Before he started a lesson, he would clear his throat and look around the room, glaring at any child who fidgeted, until there was complete silence.

He already knew Siddhartha quite well. For anyone who lived in the palace, it would have been difficult not to. Since he was old enough to crawl, Siddhartha had managed to find his way to the classroom, where he would sit outside the door and listen to the children recite their lessons. Sometimes, Mr Mohan would not even know he was there. Opening the door, he would practically trip over the baby boy looking up at him. The child's eyes were so hard to resist that the teacher would sigh, lift him onto his shoulder, and after much giggling and nudging from the other children, continue the lesson. Now that Siddhartha had formally joined the class as a student, Mr Mohan was determined that no one accuse him of having a favourite, so he decided to treat the Prince exactly like everyone else in the class.

Siddhartha was excited. He was eager to learn. At last, after hour-long minutes, Mr Mohan walked into the room and as usual cleared his throat. As he looked gravely from face to face, his gaze settled for a moment on the pert young Prince.

"Now then, Gowri Mohan," he prepared himself, "here's a bright spark that should keep you on your toes."

"Sit down everyone," he said aloud. "For the benefit of the new boy here today, we shall start with the alphabet. Do you know the alphabet at all, young man?" he inquired of Siddhartha.

"Yes Sir, I do Sir. Which one shall we do today Sir?" Siddhartha asked innocently.

Mr Mohan wondered if Siddhartha was already being cheeky. He decided to play one step ahead of him. "Which one you ask! Well now, let me see. We don't want to ask anything too easy of such a clever boy. I suppose you already know our Sanskrit alphabet?"

The class tittered.

"No," Mr Mohan continued, "that would be too boring for you. How about Mongolian or Tibetan? Hmm… No, I suppose not," he continued quickly seeing Siddhartha open his mouth to reply. "Too easy, I know.. Ah! How about some Mandarin?"

The children giggled. "Yes, speak Mandarin! Come on, Siddhartha! Show us what you know," they teased.

Siddhartha blushed and opened his mouth to speak. Before he could make a sound, Mr Mohan interrupted him. "Speak up boy! What's wrong?" He challenged. "Don't you know ANY Chinese?" and he looked around the room in mock astonishment, encouraging the children to join the game.

"Fancy not knowing Mandarin! Anyone can ask for sweets in Mandarin! Come on, ask for sweets!" came the cruel taunts of his classmates.

Poor Siddhartha waited quietly. He had been warned that everyone was tested for his courage on his first day at school, so he waited patiently for the teasing to stop. When it was quiet again, he said clearly, " If you'll all be quiet, I will speak some Chinese that I know."

Mr Mohan rubbed his nose and glared at Siddhartha. Was the boy pulling his leg?

"Well, as you're so very clever, Siddhartha Gautama, perhaps you will be so kind as to GET ON WITH IT!" he said haughtily. Mr Mohan stuck his face so close to Siddhartha's that the boy could feel the dampness of his breath as the trembling man spat the words out.

"Yes Sir!" Siddhartha said bravely, and to the astonishment and delight of the children, he spoke the strange sounds to them of what appeared to be a faultless recitation in Mandarin. By the time he had finished, he had won the children's wonder and respect. It couldn't be real. What a magnificent bluff!

There was silence when he finished. The children began

to shift uneasily in their seats. Now there would be trouble. Mr Mohan didn't like to be crossed, and surely, Siddhartha had tried to put one over on him.

Mr Mohan looked as though he had turned to stone.... He didn't even blink. After what seemed like an endless moment, he began to clap. As the class slowly realised this had been no bluff and that Siddhartha had indeed spoken in Chinese, they too, began to applaud. Soon everyone was clapping and stamping and banging and shouting. Siddhartha had passed the test with flying colours. Not only his classmates, but Mr Mohan himself was honouring him!

After that episode, the stunned teacher soon discovered there was very little he could teach Siddhartha that he did not already know.

~•~

One of Siddhartha's school friends, Devadatta, was also his cousin. After school, the two boys would often go into the woods and watch the deer who lived there. As they got older, Devadatta preferred to hunt with his bow and arrow rather than just watch the deer. But Siddhartha would not join in. One day, Siddhartha was hiding behind some ferns, watching a vixen feed her fox cubs, when he heard a scream from above. Looking up anxiously he saw a swan, her body stretched in pain, plummet to the earth. He ran to where the swan had fallen and took the injured bird gently into his arms. He carefully pulled the tiny arrow out of the creature's side and squeezed the juice from some nearby leaves onto the bleeding wound. Just as he was preparing to carry the heavy bird back to the palace, Devadatta rushed up.

"That's mine! Give it to me!" he shouted angrily. "I shot it. It's mine!" he cried.

Siddhartha held the swan out of reach of the angry boy. "This swan belongs to no one," he retorted. "She's wounded, so I'm going to look after her!"

"You have no right to interfere!" insisted Devadatta. "I had to help her. She's in pain," argued Siddhartha. "I'll tell you what," he suggested, "let's take our case to the court! The wise men there will decide who is right!"

Devadatta could hardly argue with that. All the grown ups went to the court if there was an important decision to be made, and anyway, it would be good fun!

"Okay, let's go!" he said, running ahead. Siddhartha followed slowly, carrying the wounded bird.

When the boys arrived at the palace, the court was in session. King Shuddodhana was listening to a woman complain about her neighbour's goat. "Sire, it is a filthy beast and

33

it is eating all my turnips! If she can't keep it under control, then it should be killed!" The lady raised her voice dramatically.

The noblemen nodded their heads in agreement. This seemed to them a reasonable request.

One of the wise men interrupted. "Madam," he said, "from whom do you buy your milk?"

"Why, from my neighbour here. It is the milk of this very goat!" replied the woman.

"Is it good milk?" asked the wise man

"Yes, I must admit it is very good, creamy milk," she said.

"And what does this goat eat to produce such fine milk?" he continued.

"Why my turnips – mainly," answered the woman.

Everyone in the court laughed. Suddenly, the woman's complaint seemed very silly.

"Then I suggest that you come to some arrangement with your neighbour. You exchange some of your turnips for some of her goat's milk. The goat will then get his dinner so he will not need to trample your garden and you will get the milk of which you are so fond. That way, both you and your neighbour will benefit."

The King smiled and nodded in agreement and the woman and her neighbour left the court together.

Siddhartha and Devadatta had been standing patiently at the back of the queue, but Siddhartha, afraid that the swan might die before their case was heard, pushed his way through the crowd. Everyone in the room stopped talking as they saw the curious sight of the two small boys with the injured swan. It was quite an unusual scene for a courtroom.

"Well, young Princes, what can we do for you?" asked the oldest and wisest of the wise men.

Each boy told his side of the story and when they had finished the wise men carefully considered what they had heard.

"If a man hunts an animal and shoots it, it rightfully belongs to him," said one. The people in the crowded courtroom nodded their heads. This is fair, they thought.

"Yes, this is true. But Siddhartha found the bird first. Surely, then it belongs to him," said another wise man. There was a lot of mumbling as people pondered both sides of the issue. "Ah, but it wasn't his bow and arrow that shot it in the first place," someone shouted.

"Yes, that's right!"

"The swan belongs to Devadatta! Give it to Devadatta!" came the people's cries.

The oldest and wisest man raised his hand for silence. "You are forgetting one thing my friends." he said as he stroked the swan's head, "The bird still lives! A life cannot belong to someone who is trying to destroy that life. A life must belong to the one who is trying to save it! Therefore, the swan's place is with Siddhartha!"

"He's right!"

"I never thought of that. It makes sense."

"Let the swan live."

"Let it live!"

"Give the swan to Siddhartha!"

The King and the noblemen were pleased with this verdict and so the argument was settled.

Siddhartha's compassion had saved the innocent creature. He cared for the swan until she was well enough to fly again, but by then, she had grown so fond of her hero that she never flew far from the palace lake.

~•~

As Siddhartha grew up, his fame spread across the land. The King was immensely proud of his fine son, but he was also secretly worried. It seemed as if Siddhartha was just too good to be true!

CHAPTER FOUR

Memories and a Plan

The King was a good man. He cared about his people and that was why he was worried. He was still young, strong and healthy but like everyone else, he could get sick and he would get old and naturally one day die. What would his people do then? He wanted his son to rule the kingdom. He would make a marvellous King and already the people loved him. But what if Siddhartha was destined to become something even greater than a King?

These thoughts had nagged the King even before Siddhartha's birth, when there had been so many signs surrounding his wife's pregnancy. What could he do to prevent fate from running its course and anyway what could Siddhartha become that would be greater than a King?

It was early evening and he had gone for a solitary stroll in the hills behind the palace. As he stood high upon a ridge, he could see the palace below him, glinting in the setting sun. Beyond were the distant peaks of the Himalayas, crusty white. The air was cooler now. The King enjoyed this time of day when the palace work was over. Sometimes, he would bring Siddhartha with him. Together they would rough and tumble on the grass, the boy always laughing and happy. But this evening the King wanted to be alone to think about his son's young future. Siddhartha was still a boy, but he would soon become a young man. The King must be prepared for his son's growing needs or else the boy would get restless.

He sat on his haunches with a blade of grass between his teeth, for the moment just an ordinary man with ordinary problems and as his eyes focused on the distant mountains, his mind travelled back in time. He recalled his wife's dream and the predictions of the Sages. He remembered the great joy everyone experienced on the day Siddhartha was born and he remembered Kala...

~•~

Kala was a magician. He lived in a cave in the foothills of the Himalayan mountains, where he practised magic assisted by his nephew, Nalaka. One day, Kala was sitting outside his cave. He had just finished breakfast and was now staring at his empty bowl. Slowly, the bowl began to rise until it was level with the magician's chin. He chuckled. This was an easy trick and he loved to play tricks with this nephew. He was just about to send the bowl into the cave where Nalaka was

cleaning when the most extraordinary thing happened. A
fierce wind came from nowhere and storm clouds gathered.
Then, just as suddenly, the wind dropped and the clouds
parted like gigantic curtains to reveal the gods partying!

The sky was filled with dancers. Beautiful fairy creatures
spun and soared through the air to wild fairy music. A gold-
en dragon seemed to be juggling globes of crystal light and
rainbows lit the sky like neon signs. A heavenly messenger
made entirely of light flew towards Kala who had to shield
his eyes from the glare. With his flowing robes flapping like
flags, the herald raised a wind that dissolved the clouds into

vapour. The vapour swirled and swelled to form a vision. Then, there was sudden peace. Kala saw a beautiful garden and a royal Queen with a newborn babe in her arms. He saw a magnificent palace set in a fertile valley. Again came the wind, blowing stronger and stronger. Kala thought he heard bells, or was it laughter? He had to bend over double against the force of the wind.

Then suddenly, it was over. A sparrow flew across the sky as if nothing had happened. The broken pieces of the bowl lay in front of Kala. Nalaka came out of the cave and exclaimed at his uncle's unusual carelessness.

Ignoring the boy's remark, Kala said slowly, "They were trying to tell me something. Something had made them happy, something to do with a palace and a baby boy."

He turned to the puzzled face of Nalaka, grabbed the boy's hand and said "Come! We must fly!"

And that is what they did. Kala launched himself and the bemused boy into the air and they flew off, looking like a pair of bedraggled black swans.

Soon they landed amidst a clump of trees. Kala and Nalaka walked the rest of the way to the palace gates where a crowd gathered, hoping to catch a glimpse of the royal family. Pushing their way to the front, the mysterious strangers presented themselves to the guards who felt themselves compelled to let them through. Without a word, Kala walked straight on towards the palace, with Nalaka jogging at his heels, nervously looking around and wondering why none of the guards had stopped them. Then, suddenly after much walking through corridors, past attendants and ministers who appeared not to notice either of them, they were

looking through a
marble archway into an
elegant, fragrantly per-
fumed chamber.

A proud King stood smiling
down at his beautiful Queen who lay supported by silken
cushions on a golden couch with a baby in her arms.

"I have come to see the child, Sire" said Kala. This day
was so special that the King could not feel fear or anger or
any negative emotion. As the two dirty, ragged people
entered his bedchamber he smiled. Then he realised that the
old man was a Rishi.

"Please come closer" he said, and lifting Siddhartha carefully, he placed him in Kala's arms.

The magician looked carefully at the child, then beamed with joy and showed him to Nalaka. Nalaka still had no idea why his uncle had brought him to this place, but he could see this was a pretty child and also a royal Prince. He slid his grubby finger into the baby's hand, who clenched it tightly in his tiny fist. "He's going to be very strong" laughed the boy.

"Yes, he will be strong" said Kala "and wise and kind. But one day, the palace will be too small for so great a man. This child is destined to discover the Truth about Life. This child is destined to become greater than any living being."

"Won't he become King?" asked the surprised father.

"Oh yes, Sire. He will be a King of Kings" said Kala, returning the child to his mother. He could no longer hold back the tears that had been threatening to wet the baby. Now he wept loudly.

Nalaka had never seen his uncle like this. "Uncle, what's wrong?" he asked, suddenly afraid.

"Nothing, my dear. Nothing. I'm just a silly old man. Forgive me. Don't worry, dear Queen. There is nothing wrong with your son. It is not him I cry for, but myself. You see, one day your son will have much to teach me, but by that time I will be dead. I'm crying because I have not created enough merit* to hear the wisdom of so great a man. I do not have the good karma.*"

Then Kala bowed and quickly left, followed by his confused nephew. The King was also mystified and did not want to let the stranger go. "Fetch him back." He commanded.

An attendant rushed out. There was a strange quiet over the crowd and everyone was looking up at the sky. Two huge birds as black as night were flying around the palace. They circled three times and flew off towards the mountains. The crowd gasped.

"Did you see that?" exclaimed one.

"What were they?"

"Looked like swans to me" said another.

"No. Too big for swans."

"Surely it's an omen!"

Everyone was talking now. The anxious servant shoved his way through the chattering throng searching for Kala, but he had gone, and curiously, no one remembered seeing him or his nephew actually leave the palace.

When the King and Queen were told of Kala's disappearance and the mysterious black birds, they said nothing, but merely looked at one another and then at Siddhartha lying peacefully in his cot, sweetly smiling in his sleep.

~•~

Frowning, the King stretched his legs and wandered along the ridge. As the sun disappeared behind the mountains, the valley seemed to melt in the soft twilight. But the King was blind to the evening's magic. His mind was elsewhere. He had returned to that time many years ago when he had summoned eight renowned priests to read the signs on his son's body....

~•~

Siddhartha liked being naked. He didn't know why his nurse had removed all his clothes, but he enjoyed wiggling his toes

and punching the air with his pudgy fists. Above him hovered funny heads and bony fingers gently prodded baby fat. The child was entranced. Now he was launched above them and he liked that even better.

Held up high, he could see the room filled with people and they were all looking at him. As he was passed around like a rare and delicate fruit, the men beneath him muttered. Gently but firmly his fists were unclenched and his toes parted. Then the game was over and the nurse bundled him away.

The eight priests sat before the King to reveal the meaning of the signs they had seen on the boy's body. The court was dismissed.

"Well?" asked the King. He was a bit nervous.

"Sire, you are very fortunate. Your son will be a great man with many talents" started one enthusiastically. "Yes, yes, I know all that" replied the King impatiently. "What I want to know is, will he be a King like ME?" There were a few moments of uncomfortable fidgeting and coughing.

"That is not completely certain, Sire" ventured a second. "What do you mean? What else could he be?" demanded the King. "The royal babe is blessed with much wisdom. He will have two paths to choose from. One will be to follow in your royal footsteps," the third priest paused. "And the other, umm …will be…"

"Don't dither, man! Just tell me!" the King was actually making everyone too scared to tell him the truth.

A fourth priest bravely came to the rescue of his friend. "The other path will be that of an ascetic*, a wanderer searching for the Truth in Life. Your son's body leads us to believe he will find that Truth, my Lord." "So, what you are saying is that he could go one way or another. Am I right?" challenged King Shuddhodhana. Seven relieved priests eagerly nodded their heads, but one of them who had not yet spoken interrupted.

"Your Highness, I cannot agree with my friends. For your son, there is only one path. You cannot prevent him from seeing life as it truly is. One day your son will see four sights that will change the course of his life. He will wish to renounce the world and seek the meaning of life. And he will find it, my Lord. I am convinced that one day you will

46

see that path is greater than the first. One day you will be glad he chose the second…"

~•~

A shooting star fell from the sky. The King was getting cold. With the words of the wise men echoing in his head, he strode back to the palace. "The palace will be too small for so great a man…"

"This child is destined to discover the Truth about Life.

He will become greater than any living being."

"… a wanderer searching for the Truth…"

"…. He will renounce the world…."

"…. The Truth about Life…."

"The palace will be too small…"

"Too small!"

"The palace will be too small!"

Wrenching open the palace doors, the King stopped on the threshold. He was frightened by all these peculiar predictions. The palace had always been his home. He had been born here and lived happily here. He would even die here! Why should it not also be enough for his son?

Tired of thinking, the King slammed the doors behind him and went straight to his room. Restlessly pacing back and forth, he finally stopped before the portrait of his wife. With nowhere else to turn, he prayed to the serene and smiling face to guide him. Then he lay down to sleep to escape his torment.

… But the King even dreamed of his son. In the dream, Siddhartha sat upon a throne and King Shuddodhana knelt before him. Siddhartha smiled and the King felt as if a spell had been cast upon him. Out of the air appeared countless fairy goddesses laughing and dancing and beckoning to Siddhartha. They sang as they playfully tugged at the Prince's clothes. Suddenly, Siddhartha rose in the air above the throne and hovered before the King, who could neither move nor speak. He said, "Father, I cannot stay in this world. You must let me go."

At these words, the goddesses surrounded him as if to carry him off. Then the King felt his tongue loosen. Not

knowing what else to do, he called for his guards. "Seize them!" he cried, and many strong men rushed forward holding terrifying weapons, but they could not harm the goddesses and they could not catch Siddhartha. As the spears pierced the air, they turned into flowers. Siddhartha and the goddesses disappeared, leaving nothing but a fragrant shower of flowers falling upon the King and his amazed soldiers…

The King awoke drenched with sweat. Panic-stricken, he

sat up. Was that flowers he could smell? Nervously, he glanced around the room, but not even a petal lay on his pillow. "I must be going mad," he thought, "But he's gone. I'm sure Siddhartha is gone!"

He shouted to the guard to fetch his son. When Siddhartha arrived, he found his father feverishly pacing the floor. "Father, what's wrong? Are you ill?" he asked. "Son, Thank the gods you are still here! Promise me you'll never leave. Promise me!" gasped the King, clasping the boy to him.

"Why should I leave you, dearest Father? Everything I could possibly want is here, with you."

The King wept with relief, finally comforted. But over the next few days, the dream haunted him. It was easy to give his son everything he wanted now, but a young man needed more, much more, to keep him happy. What could he do?

Of course! The answer was easy! Slowly he devised a plan that would ensure Siddhartha's total happiness. Then, surely, the boy's path would be clear. He WOULD become King!

The King got busy and soon became obsessed with his idea. Siddhartha would soon be sixteen, a turning point in a child's life. The King planned the ultimate birthday present.

The day of Siddhartha's birthday arrived. His father had taken him on their usual evening stroll before the celebrations were to begin. He was more excited than Siddhartha when he told him about the surprise that had been prepared for him. When they reached the top of the hill, the King pointed to the valley beyond. The early evening sunlight filled it with a golden glow. Shielding his face with his hand, Siddhartha looked. He could not believe his eyes.

"Happy birthday, my son," said the King proudly. In the

valley, as if patiently waiting, sat three exquisite palaces. Each was unique and each was surrounded by beautiful landscaped gardens filled with exotic flowers and fruits. Siddhartha was astounded.

"Dad, they're fantastic! But why three?"

The King explained, "My son, when the wind blows and the air is cold, you shall live here," and he pointed to the palace tucked behind a hill, surrounded by tall trees and high walls. "When the sun is hot and the weather fair, you shall live here," and he pointed to the brilliant white palace where large-leafed trees swayed and cool blue fountains sprayed the air.

"And in the dismal rainy season, you shall live here," and he pointed to the third palace perched high upon a hill, where many dome-shaped roofs protected a secret inner world.

Seeing Siddhartha's face, the King felt that at last he had found the answer. He wanted his kingdom to remain great when he had gone, and he wanted to protect his son from life's suffering. So, in his mind he invented a perfect world, and to prove his love, he had it built for his son. What more could a man do?

Siddhartha was still staring in disbelief at his extraordinary gift. It was a gift to satisfy even the gods. But would it be enough to hold Siddhartha?

CHAPTER FIVE

The Pampered Prince

The palaces were fabulous. It was as if they had been plucked from heaven and dropped in the valley by a friendly god. The whole valley seemed to be blessed.

The trees grew taller here than elsewhere. Their branches spread and intertwined, a bright protective, living canopy renewing and restoring itself through the changing seasons. The colours of the flowers were more intense; cradling the morning dew to their hearts, the petals sparkled like handfuls of jewels tossed in the grass. Peonies and pinks, marigolds and violets, purple irises and white daisies cast mosaics of dancing light on the hillside. Their perfume filled the air, wafting through the groves and gardens like angels' sighs. The waters of the rivers, lakes and fountains flowed like silver silk, and people said to drink it or bathe in it was to receive the elixir of life. Even the weather was kinder here.

~ • ~

The King saw all this and took it as a sign that the gods approved of his plan. So, to ensure his son's complete peace of mind, he ruled that no one should destroy the illusion he had so carefully created. Everyone the Prince came into contact with was young, healthy and attractive and no one was allowed to mention even the small sufferings of life that took place every second outside Siddhartha's world. The King had designed the palaces in such a way that allowed him to overrule nature. His son would not have to endure the sight of death and decay, for at the palaces, everything would live! He wouldn't even experience bad weather, for in the palaces weather wouldn't matter!

So, Siddhartha would not know that even the most beautiful of nature's creations eventually perished. He would not see how the crisp green apples that fell unseen in the long grass slowly softened, wrinkled and rotted to a pulpy mess; how the baby field mice who wandered from their nest disappeared overnight, easy prey for the hungry night owl; how thunderclouds swallowed the sun, darkening the sky as the rains gathered. He would not see how trees were stripped by the raging winds and animals dropped dead with the cold and damp; how the heat of the sun scorched the earth and killed the crops; how people struggled to survive the floods and droughts and fires and famines. The destructive side of life played no part in Siddhartha's blinkered existence.

With the change of seasons, the court changed homes. During the winter months, the Prince and his entourage wandered through mosaic glass-roofed gardens where the air was kept warm and pleasant, and flowers and shrubs grew in abundance. Jasmine, magnolia and red hibiscus blossomed together, protected from the cold north winds. Here in the lotus pools, red lotuses bloomed. Lulled by the music of flute and sitar, Siddhartha and his friends talked and played and laughed the days away.

Before the summer sun began to burn the earth, an elaborate procession wound its way through the trees to the white summer palace where white-walled gardens shaded white lotus pools and marble fountains spouting water cooled the air and slaked the thirsty earth. Wherever Siddhartha wandered, his tireless fan-bearers followed, fanning the very air he breathed. At the snap of a finger, a vast array of kaleidoscope coloured rugs, embroidered bolsters and cushions with tiny mirrors and gems delicately woven into the sumptuous silk were heaped in the shade of a cool eucalyptus. Siddhartha lounged and drowsed, occasionally picking at a guava, mango, grape or sweet lime served for his royal refreshment. The servants were carefully trained to anticipate his moods, so before he could tire of his endless leisure, a pastime or sport was casually suggested to pleasantly while away the hours.

Before the monsoons, the court would move again. The third palace was perhaps the most magnificent. From the outside, it looked like a fairy grotto, enticing one to enter it's jewelled honeycomb. Inside, the chambers seemed to float in silk and velvet which hung from ceilings and down the walls and over chairs and floors, inviting one to sink into the softness. Each room led to its own cloistered garden whose blue lotuses floated like painted boats anchored in the still, blue pools. Goldfish swam lazily. While the rain rolled off the domed roofs and down the deluged hills, the palace stayed snug and dry.

Life was one long holiday for Siddhartha and his court. Every day, some new form of entertainment was dreamed up, and Siddhartha often starred in the mimes and masquerades that took place. He enchanted the court with his presence, upstaging the most experienced actors. He wrote plays and poetry, songs and stories, astounding everyone with his wit and intellect. Artists and performers travelled from distant lands to entertain or be entertained by the renowned Prince and be paid by his generous father. Siddhartha's favourites stayed for the season to join in the fun and were once again handsomely rewarded. Actors, acrobats, singers, sword throwers, belly dancers, ballet dancers, musicians, mime artists, fire eaters, fortune tellers, story tellers, conjurers, clowns, jokers, ventriloquists, snake charmers, scholars, poets, bubble blowers, lion tamers, monkey tricksters and elephant riders – all passed through Prince Siddhartha's famous court.

No one appeared to work very hard during the day but at night when the Prince slept in his big, soft bed, the palace hummed with quiet activity. This was when the night shift came on duty. In the kitchens, knives and fingers clicked and snapped as piles of fruit and vegetables became sweet and savoury delicacies or crisp, shiny salads. Jumlums, jackfruits, pineapples and pomelos were peeled and segmented, drenched with cinnamon and sugar, thrown in lemon juice and ginger and speared on golden toothpicks to prevent royal fingers getting sticky or stained. Pinenuts, pistachios, cashews and almonds were roasted and dowsed in salt. Okra and aubergines, gourds and coconuts were diced and sliced. The cooks experimented with endless blends of spices and herbs. Pungent aromas drifted through the kitchens as cardamom, cumin or coriander added that something special to a chutney, a curry – or cake.

While the moon shone and the night birds called, mouthwatering dishes were arranged on golden platters studded with emeralds and pearls and gilded with slivers of edible silver. All this effort for a Prince's lunch!

And afterwards, in the washroom, a fug of steam and flying hands transformed mountains of dirty dishes into gleaming tableware. In the gardens, silent shadows swept away dead leaves and removed fading flowers, while tiny paint pots and practised hands disguised the changes of decay.

In the morning when the Prince awoke a miracle had been performed and his world was perfect once more. The pain and exhaustion, the dirt and ugliness were skilfully removed from Siddhartha's world. If he ever saw anything unpleasant he did not notice it, for his life was as real as a drugged dream fantasy and his eyes saw only what he wanted them to see.

The years passed in a blissful haze for Siddhartha. He grew handsome and strong. He became an outstanding scholar and won the praise of all his teachers. In sports and fighting skills, he surpassed the strongest and bravest of his warriors and because he remained so noble and kind, no one could dislike or envy him. Everyone approved of the King's Plan and took pleasure in spoiling the boy who would one day be their King.

~ • ~

The King decided it was time Siddhartha took a wife. He sent messengers to all the Kings in the surrounding provinces and all the Lords in the kingdom. Soon, the messengers returned, but their news was surprising. The King's neighbours were courteous but reserved. They had heard of Siddhartha and his lifestyle. It was all very impressive but they wanted their daughters to marry a real man, not a spoiled child. What could Siddhartha do to prove his manliness?

The King went to visit his son. He explained the problem to Siddhartha, who just laughed.

"Don't worry Father. I won't let you down" and he snapped his fingers. A servant stepped forward

"Please fetch me the golden bow." He commanded.

The servant ran off. A murmur ran through the court.

"He's called for the golden bow!"

"The golden bow!"

"What's he going to do with the golden bow?"

The golden bow was renowned. It took a hundred men to carry it, and it was said that even a thousand men could not

string it. Now Siddhartha had called for it. Everyone in the room stood back to make room for the men who carried the golden bow. Siddhartha remained sitting languidly on his couch. With much heaving and puffing, the men placed the bow on a bed of brocade cushions. How it shone!

Siddhartha picked it up. Everyone in the court gasped and

held his breath. Wrapping the glinting string around his big toe, Siddhartha slowly strung the bow and drew it. The members of the court were amazed that Siddhartha could draw the string with his toe! How was this possible? Everyone was stunned. An excited murmur trembled in anticipation on the people's lips as the bow arched tauter and tauter in Siddhartha's relaxed hands.

The bow was arched in his hands. Then, he took up a silver straw that lay on the couch near an overturned goblet. Nothing could be heard except the soft zinging of the stretched string. Siddhartha struck the string with the straw. For a moment, there was silence. Then an echo bounced off the distant mountains and a huge, deafening roar was heard which roused the city and all the kingdoms thereabouts. People thought it was thunder, but the news soon spread. The royal Prince had lifted the bow that only a hundred men could lift! The royal Prince had strung the bow that a thousand men could not string! The royal Prince had struck the bow and made thunder!

Of course, it worked. Within days, Siddhartha had thousands of marriage proposals. So the King decided to hold a ball. All the eligible girls and their eager fathers were invited. Before the party began, each girl was introduced to Siddhartha. One by one, they nervously approached the handsome Prince and shyly bowed their heads as Siddhartha took their hands. One by one they filed past. The ceremony took many hours, but Siddhartha stayed patient and good humoured.

So far, Siddhartha's gaze had not lingered on any of the pretty faces, and now, there were only a few girls left. The

King began to despair. When the last girl walked forward, the King frowned at her in disapproval. She was so brazen. She held her head high and her eyes did not blink as they looked into those of the Prince. She raised her hand for Siddhartha to take and smiled at him. Instead of being angered by her boldness, the Prince was delighted. They remained looking into each other's eyes for a long moment before Siddhartha finally bowed his head and kissed her hand. The unpredictable Prince had made his choice.

The King was happy if his son was happy and so the match was made. The girl, Yasodhara, came from an excellent background and was lovely to look upon. The King did not delay. While Siddhartha danced with Yasodhara, the King firmly took the arm of her father and led him into a secluded corner of the garden.

"Now then, my friend. We have business to attend to. Come and sit with me and we will talk" smiled the King.

"I am very happy for your son. He has made a wonderful choice, O King" said Yasodhara's father, Lord Dandapani. "I am very happy for your daughter. There is no one alive who can compete with Siddhartha's excellence" replied King Shuddhodhana. "We are both very fortunate."

The two men appraised each other, each nodding

his head as he assessed the other's character. King Shuddhodhana thought to himself, "I think the girl takes after her father. He is clearly a man with a mind of his own."

And Lord Dandapani thought, "I have made a good match. This man is very rich!"

They both felt more relaxed now, each feeling the other to be reasonable and with much to offer. Soon they were planning flamboyant feasts and celebrations. They talked until dawn, by which time the dowry had been fixed and every detail had been discussed. Then, Yasodhara, forbidden to see Siddhartha until the wedding, was whisked away.

~ • ~

Though the following months passed slowly for Siddhartha and Yasodhara, they were soon married and settled in the valley. Yasodhara was kind and generous and her intellect a match for her man. The royal couple made a perfect couple and they were loved by all. It was not long before Yasodhara announced she was expecting a baby.

Siddhartha was nearly twenty-nine. He was a mature man now, with the responsibility of a wife and child. The King thought it was simply a matter of time before he could hand the kingdom over to his son; he had prolonged Siddhartha's childhood as long as he possibly could.

~ • ~

But, one evening the inevitable happened. Siddhartha felt bored. Recently, he had been feeling depressed for no apparent reason. He loved Yasodhara and was thrilled at the prospect of becoming a father. Nevertheless, the pleasures of the court were beginning to irritate him and he had grown tired of the endless chatter. This evening, instead of joining in, he quietly sat back and watched his friends talking, laughing and showing off to each other. And as he looked on, he saw himself; spoiled, frivolous and irresponsible, like a butterfly, flitting from one distraction to another.

He began to ask questions about the world beyond the valley. Usually, his friends knew how to be elusive and misleading about this forbidden topic, but tonight Siddhartha was insistent.

Presently, an unknown singer came forward and offered to sing for the Prince. Something about the girl impressed Siddhartha, so he agreed to listen. He lay with his head in Yasodhara's lap and as she stroked his hair, he gazed out past the gardens to the distant mountains. The girl sat at the Prince's feet and began to sing. As the story of the song unfolded, her haunting voice and gentle manner seemed to hypnotise everyone there. This is what she sang….

Give to him this token from me
Tell him our garden still grows
The leaves still rustle in the wind
And the flowers are all roses.
Say to him there's been no change
Each day I milk the goat
The hens lay warm, brown eggs
And my belly is full.

Just remind him of that day
We swam with the silver fish

He said I had blue lotus eyes
And limbs like the fleeting gazelle

Return to me, my love
Come back! I'm all alone
The world is a cold, cold place
When your heart it bleeds like stone

Don't tell him I cry every night
And swear to take my revenge
That I no longer wear the brooch
He bought in Saketa Bazaar.
Don't tell him the village talks
That they throw stones at me
That the baby grows…
Soon everyone will see.

But tell him before you part
That you thought you heard me say
When the full moon lights my pathway
I will leave here for Shravasti

Return to me, my love
Come back! I'm all alone
The world is a cold, cold place
When your heart it bleeds like stone.

When she finished, there was silence. Siddhartha's friends glanced nervously at each other. Why had no one stopped the girl? What had prevented them from crying, "Sing no more! Enough!" For a taboo had been broken.

How would Siddhartha react? All eyes turned to him and all saw how deeply the song had affected him. He had never heard of anything so sad. He wondered how people could live in such a world so fraught with uncertainty, in a world where love bred hate and joy gave pain. It seemed a place of strange contrasts.

No one knew what to say or do. Someone called for the guards to take the girl away, but Siddhartha stopped them. "No!" he cried. "Let her be!" Reluctantly, the guards withdrew.

"Tell me. Where is this world?" asked Siddhartha, lifting the girl's face to look at him.

The girl simply smiled and said, "Why, my lord! Don't you recognise it?" Then she slipped away unheeded.

~•~

In the days and weeks that followed, Siddhartha became more and more preoccupied. He would ask questions that no one dare answer, and he would go off on his own, riding on his white horse, thundering through the valley as if he was haunted. The court watched, aware that something had come to an end. Life in the palaces would never be the same again. They waited for the inevitable.

Yasodhara would sit on her balcony and watch her husband pace restlessly in the gardens below. With her hands resting protectively on her growing belly, she would wonder at the change in her husband. Ever since that evening, the seeds of discontent had been planted in his mind. Yasodhara wished he had never heard the wretched song!

70

She loved Siddhartha, and no one else could replace him. Now she was frightened. Could it be that she had lost the man she loved, the father of her unborn child, to a world he did not yet know?

CHAPTER SIX
Flight into Light

One morning, very early, Siddhartha went to the stables. "Let's go for a ride" he said to his friend Channa.

Channa was a fine horseman and a close friend of the Prince. For some days now, he had been expecting this visit. He had heard the palace gossip and could see for himself the Prince's restless behaviour. Now he was torn. He had always gone along with the King's Plan, but the closer he became to the Prince, the more he wondered whether it was right to shield such a man from reality. If Siddhartha wished to go beyond the boundaries of the palaces, what should he do? Obey the King or obey the Prince?

"I'll fetch the horses," he said.

"No Channa" replied Siddhartha. "It's going to be a long ride. We'll take the chariot."

Channa looked into his friend's eyes. His guess was right; this was not going to be another pleasure picnic. Siddhartha looked different somehow. His carefree, boyish face had changed into that of a determined young man's. Channa knew that his friend could no longer be fooled. He came to a decision.

"Of course" he agreed.

Siddhartha took the reins and Channa held on tight. Soon, the palaces were a dusty mirage behind them as the golden chariot thundered through the valley. The splendid horses gleamed as Siddhartha drove them forward, their sleek bodies steaming in the cool, white dawn. The valley stretched on and on. They had left home before sunrise and it was past midday before the palace boundaries were broken. Siddhartha felt a rush of excitement. He slowed the horses to an easy trot and passed the reins to Channa. Now he didn't want to miss a thing!

It was not long before the unfamiliar sight of village houses met Siddhartha's eyes for the first time. He looked at them curiously. Beyond the doorways, he could see the shapes of people moving about within the gloom, and he could hear their muffled chatter. The strange buildings looked like overturned cooking pots, their red clay baked hard by the sun. Skinny dogs roamed round them and snuf-

74

fled in the dirt, slumped down in the shade or scratched at their flea-bitten haunches. An old woman squatted near a pile of pans that she systematically scrubbed with handfuls of earth.

"What's kept in those huts, Channa?" asked Siddhartha. "People live in them, Sire," replied Channa. "But they are so small!" cried Siddhartha in disbelief. They drove slowly through the village. Though the curious villagers had no idea who these rich and handsome strangers were, the fine looking men in their magnificent chariot made a spectacular sight.

Soon the chariot had to stop because the entire village of people had come out from their houses and blocked the path. The people were very poor, and they thought this was a chance to get something to eat. Many hands reached up, and cries of "Master! Master!" filled the air.

An old man pushed his way to the front. "Money, Master" he whined. "Money for an old man." He shoved his toothless, grinning face up close to Siddhartha's. Siddhartha shrank away in disgust.

"Get me out of here! Take me home!" he cried, terrified of the persistent begging, the sea of desperate faces and the ugly man with the foul breath.

Channa shouted warning then drove the horses through the crowd. They left the village in a cloud of dust. The scattered people screamed after them and stones bounced off the chariot as ragged children jeered and chased behind.

For a long time, Siddhartha did not speak. His heart raced. He wanted to know the truth, but he was afraid of finding out. Finally, he said, "Who was that awful man, Channa? What was wrong with him? He looked so ugly!"

"He was just an old man, Sire. He has lived a long time. His hair has turned white, his skin has become wrinkled and his teeth have fallen out. It happens to all of us eventually. But you mustn't worry about him, my Lord. The villagers take care of their elders."

"Are you telling me that I will end up looking like that?"

"Well, perhaps not quite like that. After all, you are rich and well cared for. But think of your father! Already he is showing signs of ageing. We must all grow old one day, dear friend. That is life!"

"THAT IS LIFE?!" cried Siddhartha in horror. They drove the rest of the way in silence. Siddhartha felt ashamed. He had come all this way only to return home so soon. But he had been unprepared for the suffering of the world. For many days, Siddhartha tried to forget what he had seen. Yasodhara tried to comfort him and arranged new and enthralling entertainments for her husband, but

Siddhartha was sickened by the pretty charades. There was no more escape from reality for him. One morning, Yasodhara awoke to find the bed beside her empty. He had gone again.

~•~

This time, Channa took a different route. He wanted to protect his friend as much as possible from the harsher facts of life.

They drove through pretty woods and fields of ripening wheat. The birds called to each other and here the world seemed a pleasant place. Siddhartha sat back and relaxed. Soon, they approached a village perched on a shelf on a hillside. Channa knew the villagers in this fertile area would be wealthier than in the last.

When they arrived at the village, they slowed down.

People came out of their houses to stare. They smiled and waved and Siddhartha returned their greetings. He was happy to see the people looking well fed and clean, the houses more spacious and airy.

Channa breathed a sigh of relief as they began to leave the friendly village behind them. But, just as they turned a bend in the road and left the last cluster of houses, they came across a house set apart from the rest. In the dust, in front of the doorway, crouched a woman, a leper.* At first, Siddhartha thought she was old, like the old man he had seen. But her hair had not turned white, and although her skin was scarred and pitted, it did not look wrinkled. Flies crawled undisturbed on the open sores around her mouth while the woman's wasted arms hung lifelessly by her side. Her glazed eyes looked beyond the chariot as if it were invisible.

"Stop!" cried Siddhartha. He was shaking as he gazed upon the hideous sight of the woman. He leaned out to her. "What is wrong with you?" he asked softly.

"Money, Master! Help a sick woman" she moaned and began to drag herself forward in the dust, guided by the sound of Siddhartha's voice.

"Sire, Stay back, or you may catch her disease!" warned Channa.

Siddhartha was confused and upset. He didn't know what to do to help the woman and he was terrified of catching the disease. He took a bag of gold out of his tunic and dropped it at her feet. The piteous creature scrabbled around in the dust. Siddhartha looked as if he might faint. Quickly, Channa turned the horses around and made for home.

When they had left the village far behind Siddhartha spoke. "Tell me about sickness, Channa" he said in a whisper.

"Sometimes, my Lord, the body stops functioning normally or we may catch a disease from dirty food or even from the air we breathe. Then, we get sick."

"Do many people get sick?" Siddhartha asked anxiously.

"It is quite common.. All of us get sick at one time or another in our lives. Some of us are lucky and quickly recover. Others, like that poor woman, are not so lucky. But don't worry Sire. You are well protected in the valley. It is unlikely you will ever suffer so badly."

"Unlikely but not definite! If what you say is true, then even at this very moment I might be getting sick! It seems to me that the world is a dangerous place. We had better go home!"

So, they returned once more to the safety of the valley.

~•~

Home again, Siddhartha threw himself into palace life, as if he wanted to fill each waking moment with action, for then there was no time to think.

But it was impossible! When he looked at his young friends, he saw old men. He held Yasodhara in his arms, but felt only the skinny body of the sick woman. The delicious foods served to him tasted of dust, and even the pure air of the valley seemed polluted now.

"Why can't we stay young and healthy?" he thought longingly, and he began to understand his father's reasoning. If the world outside the valley was reality, he did not like the real world!

He spent hours alone in his room thinking. He thought about the terrible suffering of the poor, sick woman until silent tears fell from his eyes. And he fantasised that he became ill. He saw himself grow ugly and imagined that Yasodhara turned away from him in revulsion. He saw his father anxiously pacing the floor of the sick room while he lay, helpless, unable to move or speak – a useless invalid. Siddhartha felt sick with fear and he began to sweat. His mind moved on to the old man and how old age would become a reality for himself and everyone he loved. Life suddenly seemed so cruel, yet he still felt compelled to learn more. He could not turn his back on life. He must go out again!

~•~

Channa was ready. He planned to take Siddhartha to Kapilavastu. If Siddhartha wanted to know everything about life, then only the city would show it to him. He had already sent word that the royal Prince was planning a visit. On the day Siddhartha summoned him for the third time, he sent his fastest rider ahead to warn the people and prepare the streets.

Kapilavastu was an exciting place. Of course, the Prince would see suffering but he would also see the colourful bazaars and busy streets, peaceful temples lit with candles and smelling of incense, parks where children played and schools where children learned. Channa wanted Siddhartha to see life in all its wonderful shades of light and dark. The Prince was dwelling on the dark side.

As they drove through the city gates, cheers rang out. Siddhartha was thrilled to see how the city welcomed him. The streets were lined with flags and banners. Flower garlands of marigold and jasmine decorated every doorway. The people had prepared well. Channa smiled to see the happy surprise on his friend's face.

The chariot slowly made its way through the cheering throng. Siddhartha waved as rose petals were thrown at the horses' feet, delighted to see the happy faces. But as he looked more carefully, he saw that though some smiled, their eyes looked sad, that though some cheered their voices were

feeble and that some neither smiled nor cheered but stood with their mouths open, struck dumb by the enviable sight of a chariot made entirely of gold and a Prince as glamorous as a god.

Channa could not have planned a better scene to show his friend what a mixed bag human life was. But Siddhartha saw more than Channa thought he would. He lifted the dark veil of self-deception that had blinded his vision for so long, and for the first time saw clearly. Behind the smiles and superficial gaiety were lifetimes of struggle and hardship. He realised then that nothing was as it appeared to be. As Siddhartha looked at the cheering faces bobbing up and down he felt he was passing through an ocean of sorrow.

Presently, they drew near to the river, where Channa stopped. Here the cheers faded and the crowds thinned, for this place was a sacred spot. On the deep steps leading down to the river's edge, a bonfire burned. Around it, women wept. Siddhartha stared at the sight, wondering at the women's tears.

"Why are they crying, Channa? Are they cold?" he asked doubtfully, for the sun shone brightly and he could not understand the need of a fire.

"Look closely, my Lord," said Channa.

As Siddhartha stared into the fire, his eyes became accustomed to the glare and smoke. Within the flames, he could see what looked like the charcoaled remains of a human body. He gripped the sides of the chariot. He could clearly distinguish two blackened feet sticking out from beneath the burning sheet. As the flames took hold, the leg bones arched

in the searing heat and the feet lifted uncannily into the air.

Siddhartha could not speak. He fell back in his seat and Channa quietly led him away from the funeral pyre to complete the tour of the city. But the sights that remained made no impression on Siddhartha and his smiles and waves were now mechanical. When they had left the city to begin their journey home, he turned to Channa.

"They were burning someone, Channa!" he exclaimed astounded. "Why?"

"The man was dead, my Lord. If he had been left to rot, his body would have stunk in the heat."

"What do you mean? Dead?!"

"Everyone who is born must die. When life is finished, then there is death. People die of sickness or old age. When the body ceases to function, the heart stops beating and the lungs stop breathing. If you are lucky and take care of your health, you will live a long time, but eventually you too, will die. It is nature's way of renewing life, my Lord! We must all learn to accept death, for there is no escape."

"No escape!" said Siddhartha. "I don't believe it! There must be an escape from such suffering!"

~•~

This final shock sent Siddhartha into a deep depression. Channa's words would return to him again and again during the dark and fearful nights that followed. "No escape" he thought, "no escape from life and death!"

Then he realised what a fool he'd been and now he felt angry with his father for playing such a trick on him. All this time, he had never guessed the truth! He had simply trusted

84

and accepted what was shown him. He looked back on his life and recalled strange events, which had never been clearly explained. He remembered childhood experiences, which only now meant something to him. What had happened to the old, blind man who took care of the horses? Was he now dead? He had been so kind to the Prince – and now Siddhartha didn't even know what had happened to him! But he did remember the wounded swan and how he had stopped Devadatta from killing her, and how he had nursed her back to health.

And what about his mother? Why had she died, and why did no one ever talk about her? He remembered all the pets and all the friends who had mysteriously, inexplicably, disappeared from his life. He had been told they had "gone away" but he had often wondered why some of them had not said goodbye. What had really happened to them?

And where was he when he was needed? Why had he never thought of these things before? Had he been so cosseted that his mind had become numb? He could see now that youth and pleasure were powerful drugs. But now his youth was passing and pleasure could no longer satisfy him when he knew it must end in pain. Channa had said there was no escape from all this unpredictable suffering and change, but he could not believe him. Someone, somewhere must have the answers to life's questions. He was determined to learn more.

So, for the fourth time, he and Channa drove the chariot out of the valley.

~•~

They hadn't gone too far when an ascetic approached. Siddhartha noticed that he did not seem to be impressed by the golden chariot and its wealthy riders. In fact, he appeared not to even notice them! With his eyes fixed firmly on the path ahead, he seemed more calm and serene than anyone Siddhartha had yet met. He was dressed in a simple robe and his hair was long and knotted.

"Here is someone special" Siddhartha thought. " He doesn't even care what he looks like! He has no vanity and he isn't envious of my wealth! Though he is obviously very poor, life's suffering does not show upon his face."

"Channa, who is this man?" he asked when the man had passed on.

"He is a wandering ascetic, my Lord. He has

86

renounced the worldly pleasures to seek the meaning of life. He practises keeping a pure heart and a pure mind."

Instantly, Siddhartha knew what he had to do. His path was clear!

"Turn around! I need go no further. Take me to my father's palace!"

~ • ~

King Shuddhodhana had been told of his son's excursions and had privately resigned himself to the future. He could not prevent the inevitable. He wasn't even angry with Channa because he understood the charioteer's dilemma. He had always been a loyal friend to Siddhartha.

When the King heard his son's approach, he dismissed his ministers and waited for Siddhartha to come to him, knowing already what he would say.

"I must talk to you, Father," said Siddhartha, bursting excitedly into the room.

"I know, my son. Sit down" the King replied wearily.

"I've been out. I mean outside the valley," continued Siddhartha, sitting nervously.

"Yes, I know."

"I've seen the real world, Father. This was all a lie! Why did you do it? Why?" and Siddhartha jumped up, too distraught to stay still...

"Because I love you." the King was genuinely sorry and felt almost relieved that at last the truth was out. The burden of his deception had become too great to bear, but he had still not given up the hope of not losing his son.

"I know you want to see the world," the King continued.

"It's understandable. But come back! Go for a while and when you've found your answers, return and be King," he begged.

"I can't promise anything. You know that. You have had your way; now I must have mine. Give me one good reason to stay!" challenged Siddhartha.

"That 's easy! You have responsibilities. Ties! Your wife! Your child! Me! And what about the kingdom? It needs a wise ruler. What will happen to it when I am dead? If you abandon us, what will become of everything I've worked so hard for? You can't just leave like that!"

Siddhartha was tormented. His father had pinpointed his weakness. The thought of leaving his family was torture to him.

"I know all this," he said "but something in my heart tells me I *must* leave. I can't say why exactly, but I know the answers I am looking for cannot be found by a King living in a palace. It's something that goes beyond reason. I *feel* it! Don't you understand?"

Knowing the prophecies and omens much better than Siddhartha, the King indeed understood. Still, he said, "I don't understand why you must make a choice. Can't you compromise?"

"Does life make compromises, Father? Does it? I have seen the things you tried to hide from me all this time and I cannot forget them. I have seen old age and now I see it in everyone around me. I have seen sickness and now I fear it will happen to me. I have seen death and I feel it creeping up on me in the darkest hours of every night. And I have seen someone who has the same knowledge as I, yet he still smiles.

If I promise to stay on, can you guarantee I won't die? Or

get sick? Or get old? If you can, then, all right I'll stay! But if not, I must seek the meaning of life." He knew his father could not keep such a promise.

"You know you're asking the impossible. I can do nothing more for you, Siddhartha. But you must understand one thing. I did all this for your sake. I wanted to protect you. Don't you see?"

"Yes, I see. But it was not all only for me, Father. You also did it out of your own pride and ambition. We are different people – I am not you! I cannot live my life for you. No! I have made my decision. I will renounce the world to seek Truth. I can't live in *this* world any longer!" And he gestured around the richly decorated chamber with distaste.

"You must let me go!"

The King's blood ran cold. Those words. Where had he heard them before? Then he remembered the dream, the teasing goddesses, the falling flowers and his son's strange powers. Other words returned to him. In his mind he saw the quiet young priest calmly telling him of his son's destiny. "Your son will see four sights which will change the course of his life. He will wish to renounce the world and seek the meaning of life."

The King sighed and his head dropped forward. With tears welling up in his eyes, he spoke softly. "All right. Go! But don't forget, I will always be here waiting for you to return."

Siddhartha rushed forward and flung his arms around his father. They clung to each other. Then, the Prince left the palace without looking back.

CHAPTER SEVEN
Desires and Decisions

Sitting on the roof of the palace, brushing her long, dark hair was a young kitchen girl called Kisa. She had escaped from a pile of onions and a chopping board, and while the cook cursed her, she basked in the sunshine, enjoying a few moments of stolen freedom. As she brushed she hummed a tune and thought about the handsome Prince.

Ever since she had come to work at the palace and had seen the Prince, she had been in love. Kisa thought he was the most wonderful man she had ever seen. Of course, all the girls were in love with Siddhartha, but she thought their silly infatuations were nothing compared to her deep feelings. If only she could make him notice her, he would see at once they were made for each other! Closing her eyes, she arched her neck, shook out her heavy mane, and daydreamed.

Kisa daydreamed a lot. Her job as vegetable girl was boring, and daydreaming helped to pass the time. Sometimes, when the kitchen got unbearably hot, the cook's temper got hot, too. Then everything always seemed to be Kisa's fault. Even if the milk curdled, Kisa was to blame! All she ever seemed to do was chop vegetables.... Chop, chop, chop day

in and day out,
and   sometimes
through the night, too!
She examined her poor
hands. The nails were ragged
and chipped. Her fingers were
scored with brown lines, stained with vegetable juice and
they stank of onions. She sighed with frustration. These
were *not* the hands of a future princess!

Kisa rose to go reluctantly. If she didn't get back to work
soon, there'd be trouble – if there wasn't, already!! Then, she
thought she heard horses' hooves approaching, so she curiously leaned out over the balustrade to see who it was. She
could make out a young man on a white horse. It must be

the Prince! The Prince! Siddhartha was galloping towards the palace. Now was the chance she dreamed of!

If only he would notice her! She smoothed down her dress and pinched her cheeks. Then, sitting on her hated hands, she seductively draped herself as far over the roof wall as she dared without falling off.

Siddhartha dismounted and handed his beloved horse, Kanthaka, to the care of a stable boy. He approached the palace entrance, his forehead creased and lips tight while the confrontation with his father went round and round in his head. His father was disappointed in him, but he didn't know what else he could do! He didn't want to leave Yasodhara and the baby, but how could he take them with him? He didn't even know where he was going!

With these thoughts tearing him in two, he passed below Kisa, oblivious of her presence. Kisa was beside herself! How could she attract the Prince's attention? He hadn't even lifted his eyes from the ground. If only she could make him raise his head, he would see the sun shining on her lovely hair and the tenderness in her pretty face. Then, he would no doubt fall in love with her! She knocked a stone over the edge of the roof. It fell at the feet of Siddhrtha who stepped over it and kept on walking. In desperation, Kisa cried out. "Oh my Prince! How wonderful it must be to be your wife! How blessed to have been your mother! How fortunate to be your father! I'd be content to be the ring on your finger, for then you'd carry me with you wherever you want." Then she blushed and sitting with her head bowed after her passionate outburst, she clung to the cold stone wall.

Siddhartha stopped in surprise and looked up at the girl.

"How complicated life is" he mused. "Here I am obsessed with my own thoughts and feelings and here is this poor girl hopelessly in love with someone who doesn't even notice her! She is so in love, she envies all who are near me. But love should give pleasure, not pain! Life is clearly not so different for a servant or a Prince, for it brings suffering to both!

This young girl has taught me a great lesson," he continued silently. "For it cannot be attachment that brings happiness, but the *lack* of attachment! Only *without* the fires of passion can there be peace of mind. So, I must find out how to extinguish these desires. Therefore, I must first leave those to whom I am attached. I cannot stay here, and I *must* go alone!"

Siddhartha had been staring at Kisa for a long time. Gradually, she raised her head to peek at the Prince. The effect of her impulsive speech seemed to have transformed him, for his brow was now smooth and he radiated an inner peace.

"At last," she thought, "I have captured his heart!"

Siddhartha took an exquisite, priceless pearl ring from his finger and said to Kisa "I owe you more than you will ever know. I cannot have you as my wife, or as my mother or father. Nor can I wear you around my finger and take you with me. But here!" He tossed the ring into the air. "Wear this and I will always be with you."

As Kisa caught the ring, Siddhartha disappeared into the palace. She was overwhelmed. "He loves me! He loves me!" she cried and clutching the ring to her heart, she raced down the stairs to the kitchen to show off her treasured gift to her incredulous friends.

~•~

At the time Siddhartha resolved to leave his family, Yasodhara gave birth to a baby boy. The King was overjoyed. Yasodhara's timing was perfect! With the birth of his grandson, his hopes were rekindled. There was nothing like the birth of a child to bring a couple closer together. The King remembered how he had felt when Siddhartha was born; the bond between himself and his wife had never been stronger. They had seemed instinctively to know each other's thoughts and feelings. He was convinced that once Siddhartha saw his newborn son and the mother of his child together, he would abandon the idea of leaving.

With renewed enthusiasm, the King planned a new plan; he would organise the most stupendous celebration and sumptuous feast the valley had ever seen! Officially, it would mark the birth of the new Prince, but secretly the King hoped that in an atmosphere of great joy and celebration, Siddhartha would realise the strength of his emotional ties to his family and friends and succumb to the enjoyment royal life offered. His dearest friends would be there. The best entertainers and artists would present new and wonderful acts. The Prince's favourite dishes would be served in quality and quantity the likes of which had never before been seen. At a time when Siddhartha was most vulnerable, the King would deviously display before him everything he would have to give up if he left. Of course Siddhartha would give in! The King felt happier than he had for a long time.

The party was arranged for the following day. With the celebration for his newborn son imminent, Siddhartha knew he must bide his time. He had still not seen his son and the news of the baby boy's birth had affected him strangely. He was delighted but at the same time dismayed as he felt yet another tie bind him to the life he was trying to leave behind.

Restlessly, he wandered from room to room. His friends watched anxiously as he resisted all attempts to persuade him to go and see Yasodhara and the child. He was not happy at the prospect of the feast either. He was sick of parties and was in no mood to be sociable. However, for his father's sake, he knew he must wear a happy face.

~ • ~

The feast was exhausting, especially for Siddhartha, who had not slept for many nights, and in spite of the King's impeccable preparations, his son was not impressed. All he wanted to do was sleep and as the evening wore on, he dozed off. When he awoke, it was dark. A few candles sputtered and the oil lamps cast a yellow glow over the room. Siddhartha was surprised to find that everyone slept. It was as if the whole room was enchanted. Heads lolled amongst dirty dishes and spilled wine; dancers, singers, musicians and magicians lay sprawled on cushions and rugs. A few hours before, the room had been ablaze with beauty and splendour, yet now it was trashed and smelled of stale wine and leftovers.

Siddhartha stepped between the slumbering bodies and saw how sleep had transformed his friends. Squashed against walls and tables and against each other, their faces had contorted into grotesque masks. Mouths that had smiled and spoken so amusingly now snored and slobbered. Chins fell in folds on sunken chests and eyes that had bewitched and beguiled were now crusted with sleep and smeared with blotchy paint. Soft and sensual bodies had sunk into fleshy puddles. Someone, somewhere, was grinding his teeth. A wave of repulsion swept over Siddhartha. Life seemed to him to be the trick of a cruel magician who could make a frog look like a handsome fairy prince. His aversion for the pretentious veneer of worldly life was complete. Quietly, he left the spell bound feast and went in search of Channa.

He did not find his friend amongst the sleepers, but in the stables. The charioteer was with Kanthaka, soothingly talking to the highly, strung beast as he brushed and brushed his beautiful coat. Channa must have sensed someone else's presence for he could not have heard Siddhartha's silent approach. He turned and saw a silhouette in the stable doorway, a pale halo out-lining the

trembling figure as the full moon shone on his back. Siddhartha was like a caged pet that one day finds the door to his cage left open. Standing at the gateway to freedom, he was suddenly afraid to step out, yet unable to remain. Channa was prepared for this moment. He knew that when the time came to leave, Siddhartha would need some support.

"Can you get the horses ready and meet me at the palace gates in five minutes?" asked Siddhartha uncertainly.

"Of course," Channa calmly replied, as if Siddhartha had made the most natural request. "We'll be there, my Lord." Channa patted Kanthaka's sturdy rump reassuringly.

Siddhartha's tense body relaxed and he smiled faintly in silent acknowledgement of his friend's loyalty. For a brief moment, they stood watching each other. Then the Prince was gone.

~•~

Only one more thing remained to be done. Returning to the fateful feast, Siddhartha had to pick his way carefully through the slumbering people to reach his wife's chamber. Quietly, he entered. A lamp of scented oil burned and lit the Princess' sleeping face. In the rosy glow, her face shone serenely. *She* did not look ugly. Siddhartha thought she looked more beautiful than he ever remembered. All he wanted to do was touch her and he reached out with an impulsive gesture. Then he froze. If he woke her now, he knew he would never be able to leave her.

Yasodhara was sleeping with the baby curled against her breast. One hand formed a protective cup around the child's

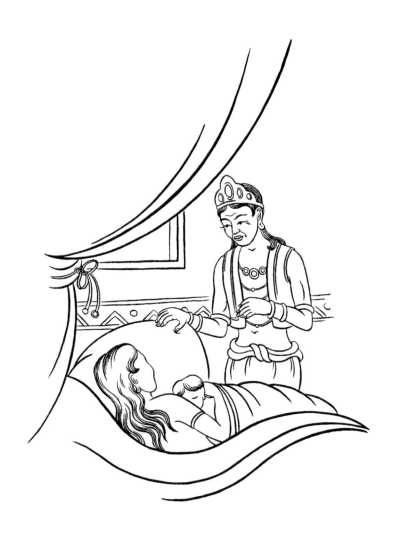

head, hiding him from view. Siddhartha strained but could not see the child's face. What could he do? He leaned over Yasodhara's body as closely as he dared and caught the delicate perfume of jasmine flowers. All he wanted to do was take his beloved wife and child into his arms! Tears streamed down his face as he fought his first fight with his emotions and desires. Rising, he realised he must leave without ever seeing the face of his only child, but he made a silent vow to his sleeping Princess. "I shall return to you when I have found what I am searching for. Then I will be able to help all those I love find true and perfect happiness. Until then, please forgive me and understand. May the gods be with you!"

Then, with the small of jasmine clinging to his clothes, he quickly turned and left.

On his way out, he saw his father tangled amongst the sleeping throng and gazed upon him for a moment. He noticed that the hair around the King's temples was indeed turning white as Channa had said, and that in such a relaxed posture, the skin around his eyes and mouth drooped.

"He's getting old." Siddhartha thought and wept to think of all the worry he had caused him. "Father," he whispered tenderly. Then Prince Siddhartha left the palace for the last time.

~ • ~

Channa was already mounted and waiting with Kanthaka. Siddhartha jumped on his horse and together the two

friends galloped away. Away from pleasure and plenty, away from family and friends, away from safety and security.... Away! Out of the valley and towards the distant mountains....

CHAPTER EIGHT

Temptations and Transformation

Strangely, no one stopped them – gates were left open and guards were asleep. Afterwards, people said the gods must have helped Prince Siddhartha to escape, for no one heard the horses' hooves or woke to see the midnight flight.

It was a fine summer's night. The black sky danced with stars and the moon hung like a huge turnip lantern smiling on the riders, lighting their path. Through the valley they galloped, quieter than the night owl's flapping wings. The horses did not tire, but strengthened their pace, the miles quickly disappearing beneath their steady tread. The friends were silent, each busy with their own thoughts. The escape seemed far too easy to Channa. He thought this must surely be a trap. Perhaps the King had gone mad in his obsession to keep his son from leaving. Even now, hundreds of soldiers could be hiding amongst the trees, ready at a word to take them prisoner! Perhaps he would even be killed! Anxiously, he looked towards the trees, then back to Siddhartha riding beside him. They should turn back. This was too dangerous!

Siddhartha did not notice Channa. His face was frozen, like a painted mask, and only his eyes burned with life. But, unlike Channa's, his eyes saw inner fears, not outer dangers. He saw Yasodhara crying. He saw his son, fatherless. He saw his father, an old and broken man. And he saw what his future could be if only he returned.

He saw himself as a great ruler. The people loved him. He had won many, many kingdoms. Soon he would rule the world…. Everyone bowed before him; he had won fame and glory! His mind was full of fantasies. There was still time to turn back. No one would have noticed he had gone, so his honour would even be saved. A million figures beckoned him – "Turn back! Turn back!"

They were now leaving the valley and climbing fast. He had a strong urge to take one last look at the enchanted place where he had lived his entire life. If only he could see it one more time he felt he would know what to do.

Suddenly, there appeared before him a panorama that encompassed everything he had ever known. Whatever he turned his mind to, he could see. As Kanthaka rode relentlessly on, Siddhartha watched the pictures move before his eyes. He saw the pleasure palaces and himself lazing and laughing with his friends, drinking wine and watching pretty dancers. He saw Yasodhara take him by the hand and lead him through the feasts and parties, and he recalled those never-ending summer days when they had lain together in the gardens. Then his mind turned to those darker days when he had first questioned his idle lifestyle and sought the meaning of life. The old man appeared as a grinning skull. The sick woman clung to his coat and would not let him go. He saw the flames of the funeral pyre reach up to the sky and out towards him, greedily grabbing everything in their path.

"No!" he screamed.

Channa was terrified. "Master, what's wrong?" Beads of sweat ran down Siddhartha's face and he looked like Death. Siddhartha clung onto Kanthaka's mane as the horse continued galloping steadily. Slowly, the vision passed. Soon, all he saw was the road ahead.

"Nothing's wrong, Channa," he reassured his friend. "I'm all right now. It was just a lonely demon come to tempt me." He smiled.

When Channa saw Siddhartha's strength of purpose restored, he, too, felt easier. Calm and clear once more, they continued their journey.

Siddhartha thought carefully about what had happened to him. In a moment of insecurity and weakness, he had nearly given in to his fears and delusions. He realised that they would always be there, waiting, like thieves in the night, for an unlocked door or an open window. He knew then he would always have to be alert, like a man who owns a precious jewel. If only his delusions could be caught like thieves, it would be easy, but to control his own mind was like trying to catch the wind! He understood then that his mind was light and dark. The shadows were always there ready to smother the tiny flame that glowed.

So, he did not look back. He had chosen his path and there was only one way to go: forward. In his heart, he carried with him the people and places he loved .. and that was enough.

~•~

They had left the valley far behind and were riding on rough and unknown tracks. They seemed to travel faster than was

humanly possible and covered many miles. As dawn broke, they reached the Anoma River, which divided theirs, the Sakya Kingdom from the neighbouring Magadha Kingdom. The horses fell thankfully into the cool water, dragging the weary riders with them. At last, on the other side, they stopped and rested on the riverbank. They had been riding solidly for nearly six hours and only now did they feel the tiredness sweep over them.

The horses drank deeply. Channa lay back and watched the sky lighten. Presently, Siddhartha rose and began to remove his princely jewellery. Taking off his many rings and ear ornaments, he gathered them together in a silk scarf.

"Here, Channa, take these," he said. Channa raised himself up on his elbow to see what Siddhartha was doing.

"This is proof to my father of my renunciation." He dropped the knotted bundle at Channa's feet.

"But Master!" cried Channa, jumping up "I don't want to go back! I want to stay with you!" he pleaded.

"No, my dear friend," replied Siddhartha gently. "I must continue alone, and you must return with Kanthanka. You were there when I needed you, and one day I will be there when you need me. It is not yet the right time for you to follow me."

Then he took his sword and cut off his long hair and beard until they were

107

just two inches long. In a joyful gesture of release, he tossed the locks into the air and ran his figures through his cropped hair and over his stubbly face.

Under a nearby tree, absorbed by the scene, sat an ascetic. He had been meditating when the strangers arrived. Having seen the rich and handsome young man cut his hair, the man was impressed. Coming forward, he said, "Friend! What you do now is a noble thing indeed. If I can help you in any way, please tell me."

Siddhartha turned to look at the ascetic. Smiling, he said, "Why yes! I think you can!"

Minutes later, Siddhartha and his new friend had exchanged clothes and were examining themselves and each other. Channa stood by watching. Siddhartha was taller and broader than the ascetic, so the simple robe he now wore fell short of his ankles, and the ascetic's new outfit hung too loose to be comfortable. He had to hitch the robe over its golden belt so he wouldn't trip as he walked. Both men looked slightly awkward and out of place. Channa, turning from one to the other, started laughing.

Seeing the absurdity of the situation, Siddhartha laughed

too, releasing his strangled emotions.

The ascetic departed with the promise not to divulge their secret exchange. He would easily be able to exchange the robes for more simple attire, and for Siddhartha, the problem of keeping his identity unknown had been solved. Together, he and Channa watched the ascetic walk away, delaying their moment of parting and then turned to each other to face their own farewell.

They didn't say anything; they just hugged. Then Channa quickly fetched the horses. Kanthaka must have sensed what was happening for he would not respond to Channa's coaxing. Instead, he stubbornly faced his master and refused to leave without him. Siddhartha went to his horse, gently fondled his ears and pressed the noble brow to his own. They stood like that, very still, for a moment. Then Siddhartha released his hold and said softly, "Go home, Kanthaka. Go home, old friend."

The horse shook his mane, stamped his foot and turned towards the river. Siddhartha watched Channa and the two horses swim back across the water. On the other side, Channa waved. For a moment, Siddhartha thought he saw a tear fall from Kanthaka's eye ... or was it just the sun reflected on the wet coat of the horse?

Siddhartha felt very sad. He could reason with the humans he had had to leave behind, but how could he explain his desertion to an animal? Somehow, this was the hardest goodbye of all.

From the other side of the river, Channa and Kanthaka watched the lonely figure walk away. Prince Siddhartha was slowly transformed into a simple and humble wanderer as his outline merged with the dusty road, growing smaller and smaller.

Channa stood watching until his image became a mere speck on the horizon. The royal Prince Siddhartha had already gone forever, and as the dark speck vanished into emptiness, Channa wondered who, and what, his friend would be if they ever met again.

"Two roads diverged in a yellow wood, and I –
I took the one less travelled by,
And that has made all the difference."

From *The Road Not Taken* - a poem by Robert Frost

Afterword

The intended purpose of *Ten Thousand Days of Summer* is to inspire you, dear reader, as the life of Siddhartha has inspired me. I was a searcher for "something more" when his story entered my life, and you may be too. His life showed me that if we are fortunate enough to be born with choices then sometimes the obvious choices we are offered are not the only ones available. There are many ways to live. I was given two paths in life: one that was laid out before me as expected – get a well-paid job, settle down and have a family, buy a nice house, car, and keep out of trouble; or one that was less obvious and unknown even to me: one that was motivated by the wish to find my true purpose in life – my quest. I eventually chose to pursue the second, after many wrong turnings, because it gave my life more meaning. It did not prevent me from having all those things, but put them in their place.

In the first part of his life Siddhartha has identified what he is searching for but he is just beginning on the journey to find his treasure. He has to overcome many obstacles, study, learn and go through challenges and trials before he finds what it is he is seeking. But he does get help. Many along the way support Siddhartha in his quest. None of us are ever alone. In my second and third books of "The Buddha" trilogy you will find this out. After all, there are over eighteen thousand days of his life left for me to tell you about.

This first book ends at arguably the hardest part of Siddhartha's adventure, when he commits to the path "less travelled by", and burns the bridges to turning back and changing his mind. He chooses to follow his intuition even though it means leaving a fabulous comfort zone and entering hardship and the unknown. Quests are not easy choices. They are neither fantasy computer games nor armchair entertainments, nor temporary thrills like bungee jumping or white water rapid rides. They are not adventure holidays. They are reality and they are for life. To be the hero or heroine of your own story – following your heart when others pressure you to do otherwise – takes courage, determination and self-belief.

If you are a fortunate one, you will be facing many difficult decisions too as you enter adulthood, and I sincerely hope that this little book is one of your helpers in life, supports you to make good choices and lifestyle decisions, and that you find your own treasure, whatever it is you seek. It took Siddhartha twenty-nine years to even leave home, so, hey, no rush!

I also wish you happiness and the fulfilment of your own quest. In the words of my wise teacher and role model, Lama Thubten Yeshe: "It is a simple truth that if we identify ourselves as being fundamentally pure, strong and capable we will actually develop these qualities, but if we continue to think of ourselves as dull and foolish, that is what we will become."

The Author

Glossary

ascetic   Person who practises self-denial (not giving in to pleasures of the senses) as a religious discipline

buddha   A fully enlightened being: one who has removed all negativities and developed only positive qualities to perfection. Buddhism teaches that we are all capable of becoming a buddha

chapatti   Flat soft unleavened bread, widely used as a basic food in Indian cookery

dharma   Buddhist teachings that protect us from suffering and dissatisfaction

karma   Actions: causes and their effects. Positive actions (good karma) produce happiness and negative actions (bad karma) lead to dissatisfaction

leper   One who has leprosy, an infectious

disease of the skin that can lead to disfigurement

merit Good karma

nirvana The state of complete freedom from ordinary existence and its cycle of dissatisfaction and suffering. This is achieved by one who becomes a buddha

Om Namo Shiva-ji A short prayer to Shiva, one of the Hindu gods, said as a request and a reminder for his blessings

rishi One with supernatural powers gained through meditation, such as the power to fly or to move objects without touching them

sage A person of profound wisdom, attained through reflection and experience

Shakyamuni Buddha
(563-483BCE) The 'enlightened one' of the Shakya clan. Buddha Shakyamuni is the founder of what came to be known as Buddhism.

Bibliography

Bays, Gwendolyn. *The Voice of the Buddha: The Beauty of Compassion* (translation of the Lalitavistara Sûtra), 2 Vols. Berkeley, CA: Dharma Publ., 1983.

Based on: 1) French translation from the Sanskrit and Tibetan by Edouard Foucaux (1884), 2) Eighth Century translation from Sanskrit into Tibetan by Jinamitra, Danasila, Munivarman and Yeshes Sde, 3) *The Blue Annals, The Stages of Appearance of the Doctrine and Preachers in the Land of Tibet 'Gos lo-tsa-ba (1392–1481)*, George N Roerich

Conze, Edward. *Buddhist Scriptures, Selected and translated*, Penguin Classics, 1971.

Lama Thubten Zopa Rinpoche. *Twelve Events of Guru Shakyamuni's Life, An oral teaching at Kopan Monastery*, Kathmandu, Nepal, November 1974

Obermiller, E. tr. *The History of Buddhism in India and Tibet by Bu-ston*. Delhi: Sri Satguru Publications, 1986.

Saddhatissa, Hammalawa. *The Life of the Buddha*. Mandala Books, Unwin Paperbacks, 1981

Thomas, Edward J. *The Life of Buddha as Legend and History*. London: Routledge & Kegan Paul, 3rd ed., 1949.

Andrea Willson and Andy Weber

About the author

Andrea Willson is a teacher, consultant, author and story-teller. In 1980 she was working as an English & Drama teacher when she went on a course about Buddhism. She was so convinced of its message that she gave up her job and sold her house in order to move into and study at a Tibetan Buddhist Dharma centre. Andrea has also taught in a large secondary school, becoming Head of Belief, Philosophy and Ethics and is the author of educational books by Heine-mann. She started Yeshe Buddhist Centre in 2001, and in 2003 founded her consultancy through which she offers *Inner Management-* professional and personal development train-ing. Also known as "Ondy", she lives with the illustrator of

this book, and their two children, to whom this book is dedicated, in the Lake District in the North of England.
www.wellseeingconsultancy.co.uk
www.yeshebuddhistcentre.co.uk

About the illustrator

Andy Weber is one of the best-known western artists of Tibetan Buddhist Iconography. In the 1970s he spent seven years in India and Nepal studying under the guidance of Tibetan Buddhist Master Artists. His unique style is highly respected not only by the growing number of Western Buddhists but also by Tibetan Lamas, many of who have commissioned his work. His thangka paintings (Tibetan scroll paintings) can be seen in Buddhist centres and temples throughout the world including the Potala Palace in Lhasa and his images are published widely. As well as painting and drawing in his studio in the Lake District he also lectures and teaches regularly at international Buddhist Centres, art galleries and universities. Andy also has a son who lives in Los Angeles.
www.andyweberstudios.com

The distributors of this book are

www.wisdom-books.com

It can also be purchased directly from the author
and illustrator through their websites